The QUAKE PATROL

A Safety Learning Book

Written by
E. Anne Warren

Design and Illustration by
Confluence Studio

MANDATED COST SYSTEMS, INC.
Sacramento, California

This book is dedicated to the following:

Young children for whom earthquakes and other disasters are frightening, my colleagues, elementary teachers, who must teach and keep their students safe, my colleagues in the Emergency Management field, especially Fire Chief Terry and Betty Kildow and, finally, my literary cheering section—Dr. Lois Freeman, Dr. John and Eloise Norton, Leslie Kirk Campbell, Linda Davis-Jones, Dr. Linda Randolph, Loretta Neal, Laura Steiger, Barbara Miller, and Heather Little.

Acknowledgments are due to:

The educational advisors, Katherine Bailey, Program Manager, Coastal Region, Governor's Office of Emergency Services, Elaine Keating, Reading Recovery Teacher, Fremont School District, Ann Pizarro, Reading Consultant, San Francisco and Melody Stendahl, Principal, Mark Twain School, Lawndale Elementary School District.

John Schiendel, Editor
Jerome Fields, Esq.
William Kelly, Esq.

In The NICK OF TIME

This is Nikki. Once, during an earthquake, she felt bold and brave. When the room began to move, Nikki stood up and crossed her arms.

It shook her down to her toes. It zipped her and zapped her. And plopped her down on the floor.

Nikki was so scared. She forgot.
In an earthquake the Quake Patrol learned to

DROP, COVER, AND HOLD!

HOW TO BE SAFE

In An Earthquake

Our teacher shows us that people may get hurt during an earthquake. Buildings move and many things fall.

But my class is learning to be safe in an earthquake.

When the earth shakes
our teacher told us:

① **DROP**

under a desk.

② **COVER**

your head under it.

And

③ **HOLD**

onto the desk.

She told us to wait for her to say, come out.

When we came out she told us to watch for broken glass, and for fallen things that could hurt us.

When the bell rings, we will quietly get in line. Hold the next person's hand so he or she will not be afraid. We will not talk.

We will go outside, just like we do for a fire drill. We will follow the leader. We will listen carefully to the teacher.

In our school, we will walk down the hall past the library...

...down the stairs to the lunch room...

...and go through the blue doors to the play yard.

We walk all the way to the fence.

If we do these things, we will be safe.

How To Be Safe In An Earthquake
Worksheet #1

 **1** I am joining the

_____ Patrol.

(The missing word sounds like cake.)

2 The

QU __ KE PATR __ L

is learning how to be safe
in an earthquake.

Fill in the missing letters.

3 When the shaking starts:

I will _____,

_____,

and _____.

4 I will watch out for

broken ___ ___ ___ ___ ___.

(sounds like grass)

My class is getting in line to leave the building.
Our teacher tells us to hold hands.

 There are _____ children in line
holding hands.

 Put an ✗ on the children who
are NOT in line.

 How many children are not holding hands?
_____
Draw blue circles around them.

14

 Now use your crayons to draw a map of your school.

Use a red crayon to draw the way your class should leave the building.

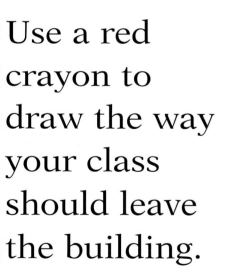

YEAAAH!

Put a Quake Patrol Sticker Here

to show you've finished Worksheet #1

WHY ? The EARTH ? QUAKES

Loma Prieta 1989

The Patrol wants to know.
What makes the earth quake?

The earth is made up of three layers of rock.

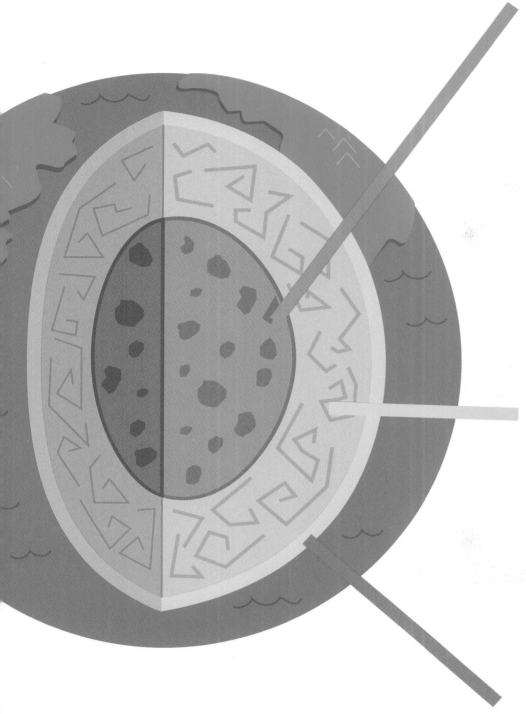

CORE

The core of the earth is hard rock in a sea of moving hot rocks and gases. It is like the hot steam in a boiling tea kettle.

MIDDLE

The middle of the earth is almost all hard rock.

CRUST

The earth's cover is called the crust. Its job is to hold the core and the middle in place.

The crust is broken into big pieces of rock called plates.

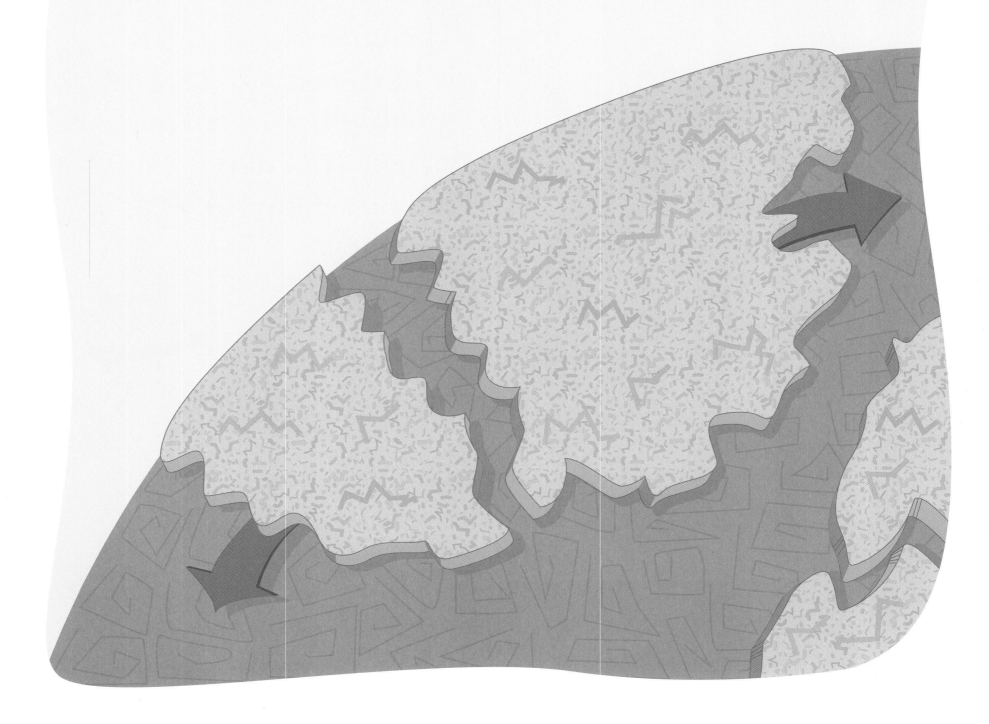

The plates slowly move away from each other.

The plates are always moving very slowly. Much slower than a snail. Too slow to see with our eyes.

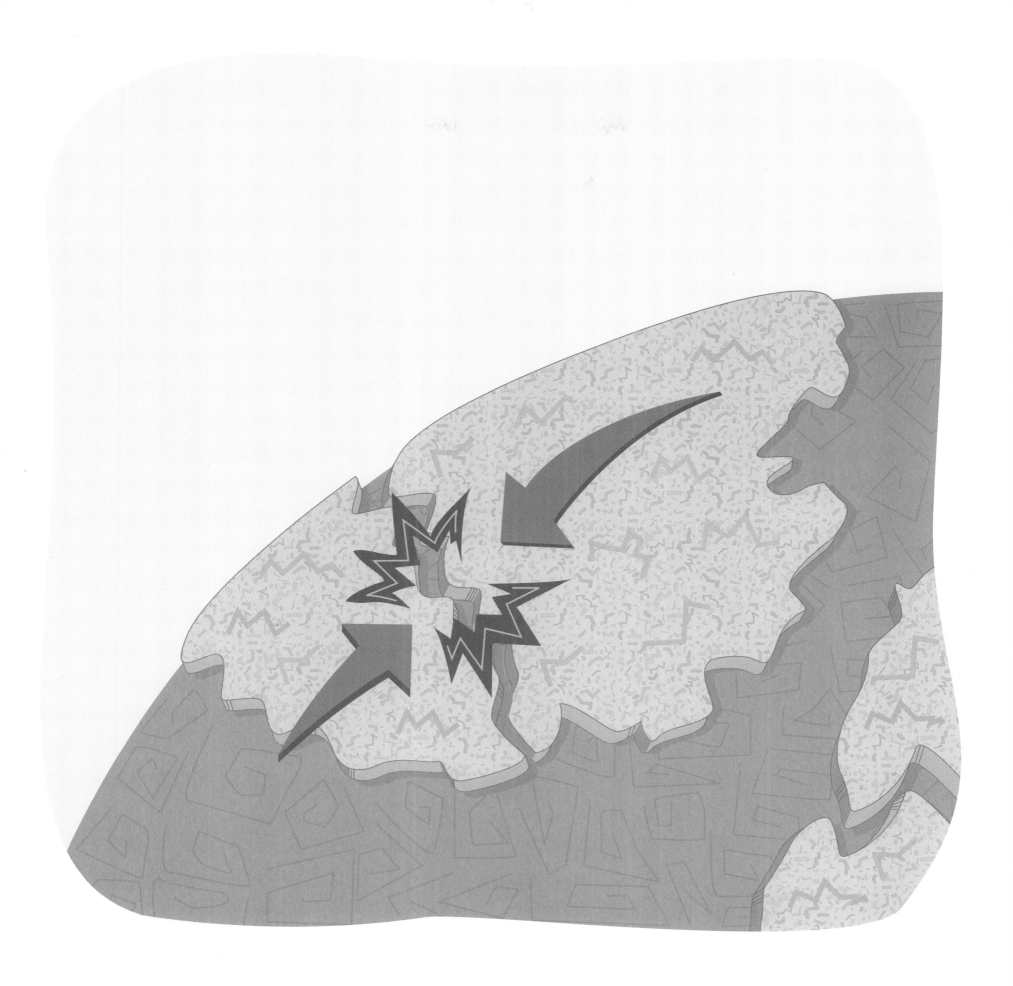

Then they slowly come back together, pressing and rubbing against each other.

When the plates press together, they create a strong pressure.

When the pressure grows too strong, it needs to get out.

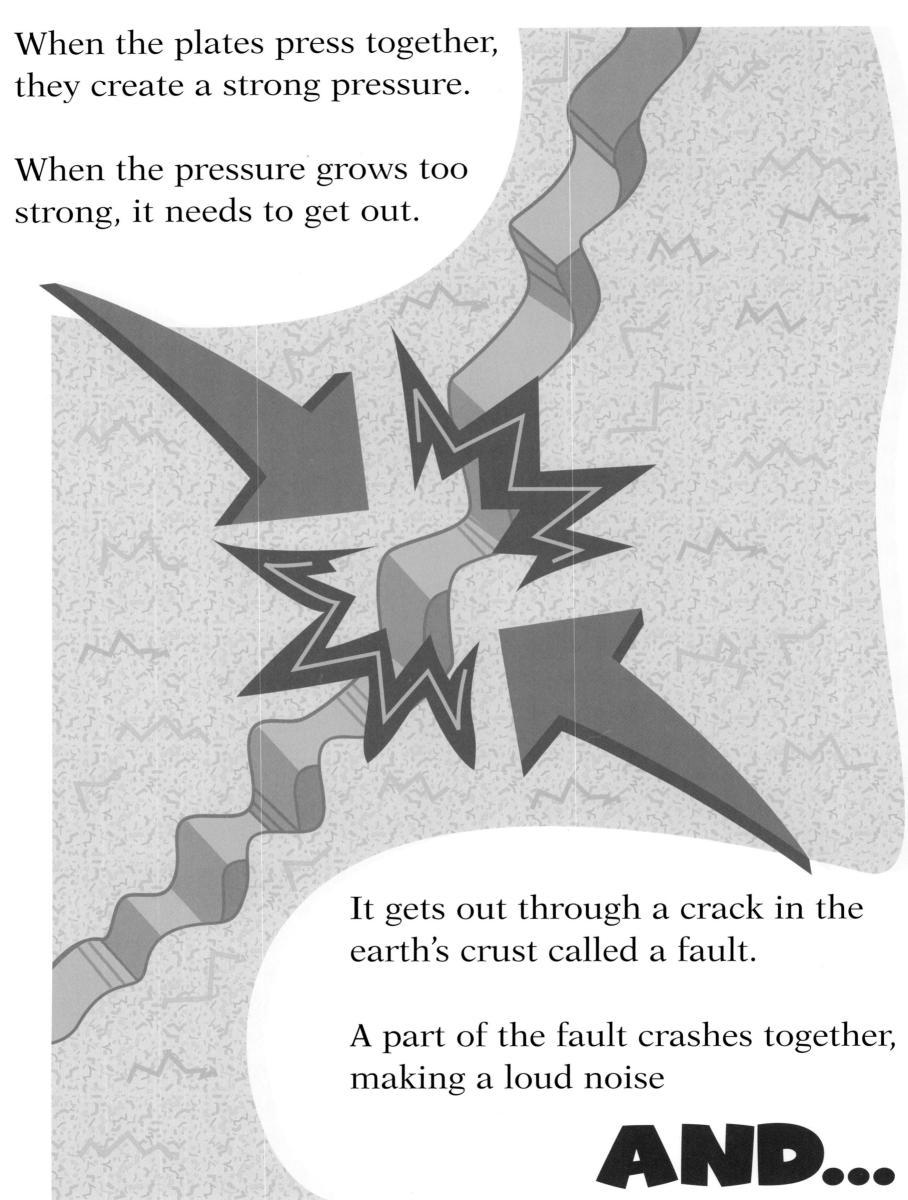

It gets out through a crack in the earth's crust called a fault.

A part of the fault crashes together, making a loud noise

AND...

A BIG JOLT!

Or it shakes, like when someone jumps on a bed while you are sitting on it.

21

1 Draw a line from the right picture to the name of that part of the earth.

CORE

CRUST

MIDDLE

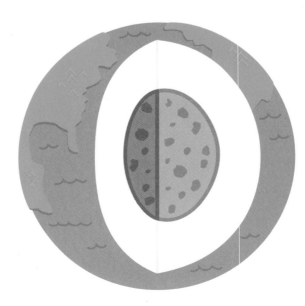

2 Find the three layers of the earth.

Color the core red.

Color the middle yellow.

Color the crust brown.

3 An earthquake fault is made when

the ___ ___ ___ ___ ___ ___ rub together.

Here's a clue

YEAAAH!

Put a Quake Patrol Sticker Here

to show you've finished Worksheet #2

The Quake Patrol MAKES OUR ROOM SAFE From Falling Things

In an earthquake there are things that can fall and hurt us.

But in our room they will not. Many things have been fixed so they will not fall. Our class is lucky.

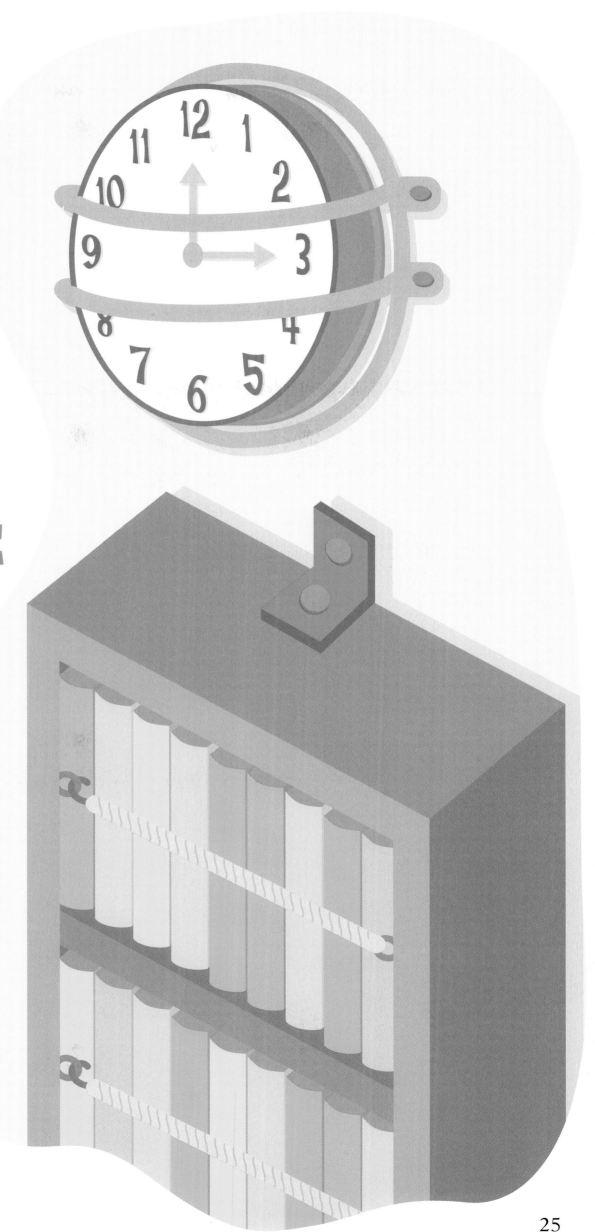

THE WALL CLOCK

THE BOOKCASE

THE BOOKS ON THE SHELF

The Patrol Checks

THE
RABBIT CAGE

THE
COMPUTERS

THE
FISH TANK

When we patrol, we put our blocks and toys in a box that closes.

We put all of our heavy toys on the bottom shelf.

Because things that fall during an earthquake can hurt us.

1 Look at the pictures and put an **X** on three of the things that could hurt us.

 **What else in this classroom could fall?**

Circle which ones could hurt us.

YEAAAH!
Put a Quake Patrol Sticker Here

to show you've finished Worksheet #3
You Are Now in the **QUAKE PATROL**

EARTHQUAKE for LUNCH

Nikki asked, "Did the earthquake shake you up?"

Mark said, "Not at first, But then I saw

My milk go scooting down the table

And heard a window crack!

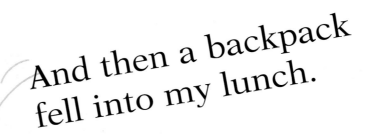

And then a backpack fell into my lunch.

It shook me so hard it made my stomach ache.

Then our teacher shouted, "For goodness sake!

DROP,
COVER,
AND HOLD!

It's an earthquake!"

Read this story to a friend. It will tell your friend how it feels in an earthquake, and how to be safe.

SUGGESTIONS FOR TEACHERS

Quake Patrol Activities *Page 11*

1. Build a model of their school using milk cartons or cereal boxes for the classrooms. Include a red line to show how the class will evacuate the school after an earthquake.

2. Have the students test the map by choosing a member of the Quake Patrol to follow the map to get safely out of the building.

Why the Earth Quakes Activity *Pages 16-23*

Have the students build a model to show how the earth's plates move against each other.

Materials needed: cardboard 16 x 20, wood building blocks

1. Lay out a large piece of cardboard across 2 tables or desks.

2. Lay the blocks next to each other on the cardboard so they are touching to simulate the earth's crust.

3. Have a student push up under the cardboard and blocks with a finger.

Discussion questions:

What has happened to the earth's crust?

How many faults were made?

What would happen to people in buildings that are along these faults?

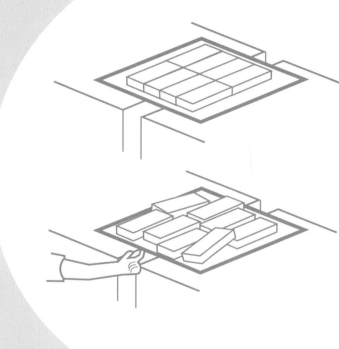

Making Our Room Safe Activity *Pages 24-29*

Have the students examine their own classroom for things that could fall and hurt someone during an earthquake.

Make a list of those things to be fixed to give to the principal and custodian.

REFERENCES FOR FURTHER LEARNING

www.fema.gov/kids
What you might feel in a Disaster

www.fema.gov/kids/little.htm
The Turtle Tale
Rumble Tumble
Rap for Kidz